CONTENTS

Copyright © 1985 Walt Disney Productions. Published by London Editions Limited, P.O. Box 111, Egmont House, Great Ducie Street, Manchester M60 3BL. Distributed by World International Publishing Limited, P.O. Box 111, Egmont House, Manchester M60 3BL. Printed in Gt. Britain. ISBN: 7235 6766 2.

Cinderella tells a story about PLUTO

1. Here is Cinderella with another of her stories. It is all about the dog, Pluto.

2. One fine summer day, Pluto was sent out to the hills to look after some sheep.

3. Pluto took the sheep to a slope covered with juicy grass then he went to sleep.

4. Falling asleep was naughty. So Pluto did not notice when a crafty coyote spoke to the sheep.

5. The coyote told the sheep he knew where there was some juicy grass and said: "I'll show you where. Follow me!"

6. "There is a lot more grass like this in my cave," said the coyote and the silly sheep followed him, all except the black sheep.

6

7. The black sheep went back to Pluto and told him what had happened. Pluto sniffed the trail.

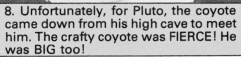

8. Unfortunately, for Pluto, the coyote came down from his high cave to meet him. The crafty coyote was FIERCE! He was BIG too!

9. Pluto ran away FAST! By a lucky chance he ran uphill towards the coyote's cave.

10. The coyote had put a boulder in front of the cave to trap the sheep. Pluto ran right over it.

11. His feet knocked the boulder out of place and it began to roll down the hill.

12. The boulder rolled straight at the coyote and frightened it away. Out ran the sheep to safety.

13. There had been no grass in the cave and Pluto, without realising had rescued the sheep.

Winnie~the~Pooh

It was winter time and it was cold. It was also Christmas Eve. Winnie-the-Pooh had prepared everything ready for Christmas in his own home. Piglet, Pooh's chum, had prepared everything ready for Christmas in *his* own home.

Now the two of them were walking hand in hand through the chilly, misty woodlands towards the home of Christopher Robin.

"Christmas wouldn't be Christmas without a visit to Christopher Robin," said Pooh.

"Indeed not," agreed Piglet. "It wouldn't be Christmas at all."

"I have no wish to be greedy, of *course*," went on Piglet, after a moment.

"Of *course!*" agreed Pooh.

"But," went on Piglet, "I wonder if Christop Robin will have a hot cup of something cheering a mince pie or two and some roasted acorns to offe his friends."

"Sure to," beamed Pooh. "Christopher Robin is that."

He thought for a moment longer.

"I do hope he has some *honey* as well."

Then he said to himself as much as to Piglet. " sure to. Christopher Robin is very *much* like that

Inside Christopher Robin's home the two frie

8

found everything their hearts could desire. There were cups of something hot and cheering. There were mince pies. There were roasted acorns and there were several jars of honey. The friends ate enough to get their strength back up, but not enough to seem greedy, of course, then they turned to speak to the others who were there.

"Hallo, Rabbit," smiled Pooh. "Hallo, Kanga. Hallo, Roo. Hallo, one of Rabbit's friends or relations. Hallo, Eeyore. Hallo, Tigger. Hallo, Owl."

He had already said hallo to Christopher Robin, when he first came in.

Piglet said hallo to everyone as well, but he said it the other way round from Pooh.

"It doesn't do to copy people," he said.

So Piglet said: "Hallo, Owl. Hallo, Tigger. Hallo, Eeyore. Hallo, one of Rabbit's friends or relations. Hallo, Roo. Hallo, Kanga. Hallo, Rabbit."

"Would you like to hang up a stocking for Father Christmas?" asked Christopher Robin.

Pooh was not quite sure.

"I've already hung one up at home," he said. "It doesn't do to seem greedy, does it?"

"Certainly not," agreed Christopher Robin, "but Father Christmas will understand. He will leave some of your presents here to be opened at my Christmas party and leave some in your stocking at home for you to open on Christmas morning."

"Oh well, that's all right then," smiled Pooh Bear.

They all had fun hanging up their stockings by Christopher Robin's warm log fire.

Then it was time to go home.

Pooh and Piglet came to Pooh's home first and Pooh said he felt the need of a little something to keep him going and Piglet said well then, he would drop in and finish off those acorns he knew Pooh had at the back of the pantry.

The two friends sat together eating their snacks and then chatted about old times.

It was a lovely way to spend Christmas Eve.

"Oh well, time to go now," yawned Piglet.

"Must you?" yawned Pooh, just to be polite. Really he was longing to go to bed.

"'Fraid so," said Piglet. "Happy Christmas, Pooh."

Pooh was already asleep.

BALOO AND THE BEE TREE

In the forest where Baloo lives is Baloo's favourite tree. He calls it "My bee tree." When the bees are there Baloo knows that one day there will be honey. All bears like honey and Baloo is no exception.

Baloo is on his way to the Bee Tree now but he has forgotten how to get there. He could smell the honey and he knew how to find it but Baloo's memory is so bad he could not remember where the tree grew. He called on his friend Mowgli to help him find it but he couldn't help. Will *you* help Baloo? You follow any paths that have been stopped and Baloo is very hungry, as you can see.

ROBIN HOOD AND

1. On a fine sunny day, Prince John decided he would buy a new crown. "It doesn't do to look shabby," he smiled. "The people expect princes to look smart." He picked up a bag of gold.

2. Crowns cost a lot of money, you know. Robin Hood's eyes shone, as he saw Prince John walking to the shops with such a big bag of gold.

3. Not knowing that Robin Hood was watching him, Prince John walked happily into the Crown Shop and put the gold on the counter. "Show me some of your best crowns," he purred. "You know the sort I like — with thick gold and bright jewels."

4. The shopkeeper was delighted at the idea of making a good sale. While Prince John was busy *inside* the shop, Robin Hood and his big friend, Little John, were standing *outside* the shop, looking at the shop sign.

5. The shop sign was a large crown, made of wood of course, not gold. Robin took down the wooden crown.

PRINCE JOHN'S CROWN

6. How the villagers stared. "Why is Robin stealing a worthless crown?" they asked. "It's no good stealing things like that from the rich to give to the poor!" Prince John scowled.

7. He wasn't scowling at Robin. He didn't know Robin was near. He was scowling at the crowns. At last, he found one he liked.

8. "This is just the design I like," said Prince John, "but I should like it bigger." "Will this do?" shouted Little John.

9. Little John pushed the wooden crown down over Prince John's arms, while Robin Hood took the bag of gold — to give to the poor.

10. "So taking that wooden crown was not so silly after all," laughed the villagers. "Good old Robin Hood — and Little John!"

Baloo plays Bat-and-Ball

1. Mowgli was a little human boy who had been brought up in the jungle with the animals. One day, he was playing bat and ball with some monkeys when Baloo, the bear, arrived.

2. Baloo was friendly and good-natured and also very BIG. When he said that he wanted to bat, no-one dared say "No". Baloo was quite good at batting.

3. In fact, Baloo was so good that the game went on for ages with no-one else having a turn to bat. The other animals became sad. *Baloo* was having *all* the fun.

4. "How about going swimming?" suggested Mowgli, whose arm was aching from bowling the coconut ball to Baloo. Baloo was amazed.

5. "Fancy wanting to go swimming, when we are having such a marvellous time playing bat and ball," he gasped. No-one noticed Shere Khan, the tiger.

6. Shere Khan hated Mowgli and was always looking for a chance to harm him. He crept closer and closer as the chums went on playing.

7. At last, it seemed that Baloo might be caught out. He hit the ball in Mowgli's direction and the jungle boy held up his hands.

8. "Oh, bother!" gasped Mowgli as the ball whizzed too high over his head and he missed catching it. He should have been pleased because—BONK!—the ball hit Shere Khan.

9. "Goodness! Shere Khan was about to pounce on me. What a narrow escape!" shivered Mowgli. They all stared at the tiger, knocked out by the ball.

10. "We must go away before Shere Khan wakes up," said Mowgli, and Baloo agreed. So they stopped playing bat and ball and went far away for a cool swim, which made everyone happy—except Shere Khan.

January

This is the first month in our year and is named after the Roman god, Janus. The ancient Romans worshipped many gods. Janus had two faces and they each looked in a different direction. He could be looking back at the old year and forward into the new year ahead.

New Year's Day is celebrated most enthusiastically in Scotland, where the festival is called Hogmanay. January has 31 days. Its birthstone is garnet.

February has only 28 day except in every fourth ye when it has 29. Its birt stone is the love amethyst.

February

The name February comes from th Roman festival, Februa. This was th time to confess your sins and be forgive or shriven of your wickedness. This wa done on Shrove Tuesday, which no comes much later in the year.

March

On the shores of the Mediterranean, March saw the end of winter and the beginning of spring, and the Romans counted March as the first month of the year. It was named after Mars, the god of war. St. David's Day is on March 1st and St. Patrick's Day on March 17th. Our first day of spring falls on March 21st. The birthstone for March is the blue aquamarine.

The first day of spring falls on March 21st. The the flowers start to bloom and folk feel happie

April

The Greek goddess of love was named Aphrodite, and April could have been named after her. Perhaps the word April came from the Roman verb aprire, to open. Many tree-buds burst in April and the ground is opened-up or ploughed to take seed. The 1st of April is All Fools Day, when tricks are played. St. George's Day is 23rd April. The birthstone for April is the diamond and April has 30 days.

On the 1st of April, when tricks are played, for some strange reason people say the word "rabbits".

May

There are 31 days in May and its birthstone is the beautiful emerald. May could have been named after Maia, the wife of the god Jupiter, or it could have been called after a Roman council of elders known as the Maiores.

There is a district in London called Mayfair, where fairs used to be held on May Day, the 1st of May, and folk would dance round maypoles.

June

We like to think of June as the month when sunny summer is really with us. The 21st of June is the longest day of the year. June could have been named after Juno, the goddess protecting women and marriage.

There are 30 long days in glorious June and it has two birthstones, the shimmering pearl and the agate.

July

Julius Caesar was a famous Roman general. July is named after him. He was the first Roman commander to lead an attack on Britain. July 15th is St. Swithin's Day. If it rains on St. Swithin's Day, folk say that rain may continue for 40 days and 40 nights, without stopping. St. Swithin was a bishop.

After his burial, some people wanted St. Swithin's body removed to Winchester Cathedral. It rained so hard his body could not be moved.

August

August is named after the Roman Emperor Augustus. It used to consist of 30 days, but Augustus increased the days to 31 so that his month had as many days as that of Julius Caesar.

The day was taken from February, which already had fewer days than other months. The birthstone for August is the sardonyx.

September

September is the ninth month of the year but it was the seventh month for the Romans. Therefore, it is named from a word meaning seven. There are thirty days in September and its birthstone is the green or yellow Chrysolite. On the 23rd September, day is the same length as night. This day marks the beginning of Autumn. From then on, nights grow longer than days and the cold winter months chill the land, particularly in the northern part of the world.

Autumn is the time when the leaves turn to red, orange and brown before falling from the trees. It is the beginning of migration for the birds who fly to warmer countries.

of the Year

December

October

We are still getting the names of the months from the ancient Romans and in their calendar, October was the eighth month, so it is named after a word meaning eight. October, though is the tenth month. The 18th October is St. Luke's Day. The 24th is United Nations Day. The 28th is the day for St. Simon and St. Jude. The 31st is All Hallows Eve or Hallowe'en.

The octopus has eight legs and is named after 'octo', the Latin word meaning eight.

November

This month is named from a Latin word meaning nine, although it is our eleventh month. The 1st day of November is All Saints Day, when it is hoped that all the witches who were around on Hallowe'en have been frightened away. The 5th November is Guy Fawkes Day when we remember the plotters who tried to blow up the Houses of Parliament. The 11th is Armistice Day, the date when the First World War ended.

December

Again we are back to the Romans who named this month. December was their tenth month and is taken from the word for ten. The most remembered date is 25th December when we celebrate the anniversary of the birth of Jesus. Hence we have Christmas. At the end of the month we have the celebrations for the end of the year and to bring in the New Year.

Above is St. Nicholas who traditionally brings gifts for children.

DUMBO
The Flying Elephant

1. Dumbo, the flying elephant, and his pal, Timothy Mouse, lived in a circus. One day, they watched Sally and her performing seals.

2. Sally and the seals were rehearsing for the evening show, but one naughty seal ran away!

3. "I am tired of doing the same thing over and over again. I want some adventure," said the seal. Off he went.

4. Although everyone searched and searched, they could not find the seal. It was now almost time for the evening show. Dumbo flew up into the air.

5. "That seal said he wanted some adventure. I wonder if he went to the sea," thought Dumbo. He swooped down low, searching the rocky coast.

6. And there was the seal, sitting cold and lonely on a rock. He was lost and tired.

7. "Dumbo!" gasped the seal. "You've found me. Please take me home."

8. "Climb on my back," grinned kind Dumbo. He flapped his big ears and soon had the seal back at the circus.

9. Sally was pleased, and the audience loved the show, Dumbo had extra buns for his supper. Clever chap!

A surprise for Sneezy

1. Snow White was housekeeping for the seven dwarfs in their pretty cottage, deep in the forest. However, Snow White said that the dwarfs had to do the tidying up work outside.

2. Snow White set the dwarfs to clearing the fallen leaves. Sleepy, though, who had been dozing and not listening properly, wandered off into the woodland.

3. "Now – yawn – what – yawn – was it – yawn – Snow White said?" he asked, as he snuggled down.

4. "She said for you to clear up the leaves around the cottage," said the forest creatures. Sleepy was too fast asleep to hear. The birds covered him with leaves.

5. You see it was a rather chilly time of year and the birds did not want Sleepy to catch cold. Some hours later Sneezy came by.

6. Sleepy might have been sleeping under those leaves all winter long if Sneezy had not sneezed just as he was passing. A-TISHOOOO!

7. The huge sneeze blew the leaves from Sleepy's face. "Goodness! You mustn't stay there," gasped Sneezy, pulling Sleepy awake.

8. He put Sleepy in the wheelbarrow and pushed him home in time for supper. "Thank goodness you have found him. We thought he was lost," smiled Dopey, Happy, Bashful, Snow White, Doc and Grumpy, while Sneezy sneezed "A-TISHOO!"

Donald Duck's New Painting

1. "Donald, I have bought a new painting. Please come and look at it," said Daisy Duck one day. Donald thought the painting was grand. It showed a pretty waterfall in the countryside. "I wish I had a painting like that in my house," thought Donald.

2. Donald said goodbye to Daisy and set off on his way home. However, he was thinking so much about the lovely painting that he did not really notice where he was going. Instead of walking home, he went out of town.

3. Suddenly, Donald blinked and stared with astonishment. "I'm seeing things!" he gasped. He rubbed his eyes, but he *still* saw the same thing. He was looking at the waterfall from Daisy's painting. Donald was delighted.

4. "The artist who painted Daisy's picture must have sat here copying this waterfall," thought Donald. "Well, two can play at that game. I will buy some painting materials and paint a picture of the waterfall for myself." He set to work at once.

5. Donald was soon to learn that painting is not easy – especially out in the country. A goat ate his first picture. The wind blew away the second. A cow licked the third and the fourth just did not turn out right.

6. Poor Donald was feeling low. It seemed he would never be able to sit and admire a nice picture like Daisy's. Then he had an idea. It thrilled him.

7. "It is the very best idea I have had in a long time," grinned Donald. He ordered all the logs he needed to build a big comfy cabin, and set to work sawing and hammering. He puffed and panted but managed to build a splendid cabin which did not seem to have much to do with Daisy's painting.

8. When the cabin was finished, Donald invited Daisy to see it. "Very nice, Donald," she smiled. "You are clever." "There is more to see yet," boasted Donald. "I have a surprise for you."

9. Inside the cabin there certainly was a surprise. It seemed to Daisy that she was looking at a picture exactly like the painting on her wall at home. Daisy was puzzled. Somehow the picture was different. It was *moving.* Daisy took a closer look.

10. Then she understood. Daisy was looking through a window at the real waterfall. "I couldn't make a good job of copying the picture," grinned Donald, "so I decided to build a holiday cabin with a window overlooking the real waterfall." Wasn't that clever!

ALICE'S FRIENDS

Alice, a rather old-fashioned little girl, had been sitting with her sister out in the sunshine, when she saw a white rabbit run down a rabbit hole.

Alice followed the rabbit and found herself in Wonderland.

She had many unusual adventures and then she walked into a garden where there was a table set for tea.

"How lovely!" thought Alice. "I would like a cup of tea and something to eat." Alice had been brought up properly and knew the correct way to behave. She could not sit down to tea without asking permission first.

She looked round and saw a wild-eyed hare gripping the hand of an equally crazy-looking man in a smart hat.

"Good day," Alice said politely.

"That's your opinion!" snapped the hare. "We don't all have to think it's good just because *you* say so."

"I was being polite," replied Alice. "It is a pity you cannot manage to be the same."

"Hoity-toity!" snapped the man. "What's your name?"

Before Alice could reply, the hare spoke up again. "Don't bother to tell him," he said. "He doesn't care what you are called. I am the March Hare and this is the Mad Hatter. Now if you want

to be friends with us, don't go on about it being a good day."

"I only said 'good day' once," said Alice. She looked at the tea on the table.

"May I have some tea?" she asked.

"You may have anything but the birthday cake," screamed the Mad Hatter. "That is mine."

Alice looked at the cake. It had one candle on the top. "Is it your birthday? Are you one year old?" she asked in surprise. The Mad Hatter did look older.

"Of course not, you silly girl," roared the Mad Hatter. "Do I look one year old? Dear oh dear, what a funny friend you are."

"I am not silly," went on Alice. "It is you who're silly for having *one* candle on your cake when you are older than one year."

"Cake! Cake!" screeched the Mad Hatter. "That isn't a cake. It's a hat" and he picked it up and put it on his head. "If it is a hat, it doesn't matter how many candles it has on the top," he grinned. "I can be as old as I like and still have *one* candle."

"You said it is a birthday cake!" said Alice. "You're crazy!"

"Of course I am. Why else do you suppose they call me the *Mad* Hatter?" grinned the man and skated round as if he were on ice, which was clever when he was really on paving stones.

Alice sat at the table where she drank tea and ate bread and butter and jam. She felt much better after that.

"Thank you for my tea and happy birthday," said Alice. "I'll go now."

Neither the Mad Hatter nor the March Hare took any notice of her. They were trying to wake a dormouse.

"I think it is time I left Wonderland and went back to my sister," thought Alice. She was right.

Cinderella's tale about Chip and Dale

1. Hallo, friends. I'm here to tell you a tale about Chip and Dale.

2. One day, Chip and Dale were out in the forest collecting nuts for their winter store, when...

3. ...Dale suddenly forgot about work! He had seen a little girl chipmunk and went to speak to her.

4. Chip was cross. He kept tugging at Dale's arm.

5. "Come on back to work! You must help to collect nuts or we shall go hungry this winter," Chip said to Dale. Dale took no notice. He just went on talking to the girl chipmunk. That was a mistake!

6. You see, the girl chipmunk already had a boyfriend. He was big and he was watching from above.

7. A moment later, Dale knew about it as coconuts showered down on him. "That's for trying to steal my girlfriend," said the boyfriend.

8. Dale did feel a bit dizzy and not very happy. The girl chip-munk ignored him and went up the tree to her friend.

9. "Never mind," said Chip. "Look at how many nuts you were able to collect!"

10. Dale chuckled. "It was a good idea to chat to that young lady!"

11. He was right girls and boys. Chip and Dale had enough nuts to last them all through the winter!

Tramp to the Rescue

1. Scamp, the son of Lady and the Tramp was out for a walk with his parents. Scamp sniffed the air and before they could stop him, Scamp was chasing some baby bunnies across the fields. "Help! Dogs!" thought the bunnies, and hopped away very quickly.

2. Mrs. Bunny watched anxiously from the entrance to her burrow. "Get indoors quicky," she shouted. "Dogs are rough and dangerous."

3. Scamp was surprised. "I'm not rough nor dangerous. I'm cute. Everyone says so," he yapped. The rabbits didn't stay to listen. They hurried down deep into their burrow.

4. "I only want a little game of chase," called Scamp. He followed the bunnies down into their burrow, thinking that it would be like his own home, light and airy and with plenty of room.

5. Scamp was in for a surprise. Rabbit burrows are dark and narrow. Lady was worried. "Scamp will get trapped," she said to Tramp. "Please do something."

6. "There is not a lot I can do," he replied. "I am too big to go down into the burrow." He called into the darkness. "Are you all right, Scamp?" "No. I'm lost!" came back the reply.

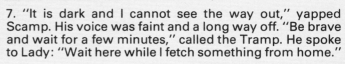

7. "It is dark and I cannot see the way out," yapped Scamp. His voice was faint and a long way off. "Be brave and wait for a few minutes," called the Tramp. He spoke to Lady: "Wait here while I fetch something from home."

8. The Tramp ran home, bounding along on his strong legs. He picked up the nicest, juiciest bone he could find and then ran back towards the rabbit burrow where his young son was waiting all alone in the dark.

9. Clever Tramp set the bone at the entrance to the burrow. Its juicy smell wafted down into the ground. "Follow the smell of the bone," Tramp called down to Scamp. Soon Scamp came scrambling upwards.

10. Little Scamp tumbled out into the daylight. "I will never go down into one of those horrid, dark, damp burrows again!" he gasped. "You were clever to think of bringing that bone, Daddy." Tramp smiled: "You may have the bone as a treat," he said.

Peter Pan and the chocolate eggs

Not so very long ago, there were living in London, three children called Wendy, John and Michael. One night they flew out of their bedroom window with a boy called Peter Pan and they went to stay for a while in Never Never Land.

Peter was rather a strange boy. He was quite old, yet he never grew up. He remained a boy, year after year. That was probably because he was having such a good time in Never Never Land. He just did not want to grow up and leave.

Never Never Land was adventurous and exciting. There were pirates and crocodiles and Red Indians living there. There was a fairy called Tinker Bell and there were a crowd of Lost Boys who were always ready to play with Peter and let him be their leader.

Peter showed Never Never Land proudly to Wendy, John and Michael. John and Michael thought it was all great fun, and joined in the rough games and excitement with Peter Pan and the Lost Boys.

Wendy thought it was a shame that so many boys were living there, away from their mummies and daddies. She decided to be a

little mother to the Lost Boys and they loved her. "John and Michael and I will have to go home very soon," said Wendy to Peter Pan.

Peter was very disappointed. "Do stay till after Easter," he begged. "I love having you here so much."

"Very well, agreed Wendy. "Until after Easter then." She sent home for some Easter Eggs from the corner shop. Wendy gave Peter Pan a tray of Easter Eggs for all his friends.

"Come on, boys, here's a treat for you," shouted Peter. Michael, John and the Lost Boys came running through the forest and leaped from stepping stone to stepping stone, across the river. It was lucky they did not fall in. The terrible crocodile was lurking in the water. Wendy saw him and threw an egg to him. The crocodile came leaping up and balanced the egg on his nose.

"He looks so sweet, I can't believe he ever does any harm," smiled Wendy. They all had a lovely Easter. Peter and the Lost Boys had never tasted such delicious chocolate eggs and when it was all over Wendy and her brothers went home. Can you find six eggs hidden in the picture?

Little Hiawatha

1. Hiawatha was a little Indian boy. One day, the Indian Chief's son told Hiawatha he must have lessons to become a good Indian when he grew up. Hiawatha was surprised.

2. But how he enjoyed those lessons. First, he learned to ride. Soon he knew how to gallop and leap across wide, deep rivers.

3. Next, Hiawatha had to learn to shoot an arrow straight and true. He even learned to shoot straight while he was riding fast.

4. "Very good!" smiled the Chief's son. "All your arrows have hit the centre of the target."

5. "You have done well and worked hard. I award you a necklace for first-class riding and shooting."

6. Little Hiawatha felt very proud. Then he saw his pony looking grumpy. "What's wrong?" he asked.

7. "I worked as hard as you," neighed the pony, "but I did not get a prize! Oh, no! No-one cheered me. It just is not fair." Hiawatha had to agree with his pony. "You may have this necklace," he said, taking it off.

8. As he put the necklace round his pony's neck, Hiawatha thought how much he would like to keep it but he knew his pony deserved it. Suddenly, the pony laughed.

9. He rolled on the ground and jumped up. "This necklace tickles," he giggled. "It isn't big enough for me. Please take it back Hiawatha, and give me a juicy bunch of carrots instead." So Hiawatha kept his necklace and made his pony happy.

Dumbo helps Angela

1. "My word! You *are* clever!" gasped Dumbo. He was watching Angela, the acrobat, balancing on the back of a chair. She was practising for the circus show that evening. Two men were working nearby.

2. Acrobats have to practise a long time. When Angela had finished, she was tired. "Will you carry my chair back to my tent for me, please?" she asked Dumbo.

3. "Yes. Of course," replied Dumbo, stepping forward to pick up the chair. Just then, one of the men, an electrician, took the chair. "Just a minute," he said.

4. "I need something to stand on, to reach these lights," the electrician said. "This chair is just the thing." But he slipped and broke the chair.

5. The back of the chair snapped off under the weight of the workman. "No harm has been done," he said, putting the back into place again and he hurried off.

6. Dumbo thought that some harm might have been done. He used his trunk and tried balancing with the chair.

7. "I cannot take the chair to Angela if it isn't safe," said Dumbo. How right he was to try and balance. The chair was unsafe. It broke again.

8. Poor Dumbo! He fell, too. Angela was cross at first. She thought Dumbo had broken the chair. Then the second man explained.

9. Angela was so pleased with Dumbo that she gave him some extra buns. "Thank you for thinking of my safety," she said.

Donald Duck's surprise present

1. Donald Duck's three nephews were in the garden playing ball when Donald called to them. "Boys!" he said. "I want you to go to the shops for me to fetch a parcel."

2. The nephews were not at all pleased. "Oh, bother," they sighed. They wanted to go on playing ball. However, they went to the shops and collected the parcel.

3. On the way home, they could not help noticing that the parcel was rather ball-shaped. Soon, they were throwing it to one another and having a fine time.

4. "This is more fun than playing in the garden," they laughed. Then – SPLASH! The parcel landed in a wet, muddy puddle. The nephews knew they were in trouble now.

5. The wrapping paper burst open and the contents of the parcel went into the water. What a mess!

6. There had been clothes in the parcel and when they came out of the puddle they were muddy and needed washing. They rushed home and began.

7. They washed the clothes and hung them out to dry before they dared see Uncle Donald. The clothes were small! "Something's wrong," groaned Huey, Louie and Duey.

8. When the clothes were dry, Huey, Louie and Duey called on Uncle Donald and showed him the clothes. He wasn't upset! "That is right," he smiled. "The clothes are to go with something I've made!"

9. The nephews were surprised. The nephews were suprised again when Uncle Donald gave them each a wooden puppet he had carved. The little clothes were for the puppets and they fitted. What fun the nephews had playing with the new toys.

'Meet Lambert Lion!' says Cinderella

1. This, as you all now know is Cinderella. She is going to tell you a story about Lambert the Lion.

2. From when he was a tiny cub, Lambert had been brought up by a mummy sheep. Lambert did not know he was a lion.

3. Lambert thought he was a lamb. One day, the farmer's boy came into the field were Lambert and the sheep lived, and started to count the lambs.

4. We all know that counting sheep sends some people to sleep. He dozed off, leaving the gate open. Out went the lambs!

5. ''He has gone to sleep without even counting me!'' Poor Lambert. He was most upset.

6. "I'm a lamb too, you know. Why is it you haven't counted me with the others?" growled Lambert, nuzzling against the boy's face to wake him.

7. "EEEEK!" squealed the boy, waking up with a start and leaping to his feet at the sight of a lion so close to him. Even *small* lions are scary!

8. When the boy made such a fuss, Lambert turned tail and ran back to the mummy sheep. Then the boy noticed that the gate was open and that the lambs were straying. He ran after them and brought them safely back into the meadow. "BAA! BAA!" they said.

9. The mummy sheep was very pleased. "If it had not been for you waking up the farmer's boy, those lambs could have been lost," she said. Lambert was proud to have been so useful.

10. I hope you liked this story. My next story for you is about Dalmatians. It is on page 56.

Baloo remembers

1. "Hallo, Mowgli. I have something to tell you. It's important!" Mowgli, the jungle boy, was floating in some nice cool water when he heard Baloo, the bear, calling to him. Mowgli looked round.

2. "What is it? What is it?" asked Mowgli, splashing to the side of the pool. At the side Mowgli found Baloo wriggling his toes in the water. "What's what?" asked Baloo. "What do you have to tell me?" asked Mowgli.

3. "Do I have to tell you anything?" asked Baloo, looking puzzled. "Can't a fellow soak his toes in a pool on a hot day without every little chap in sight asking to be told something?" Baloo has a very bad memory, as everyone knows.

4. "Only a moment ago you called me and said you had something to tell me," said Mowgli. "Now what was it? Think hard, Baloo. You said it was important." Baloo sat there thinking as hard as a bear can think when — BOOMP! A coconut hit him!

5. The coconut knocked poor old Baloo into the water. He came up and saw Louie, king of the monkeys, standing on a branch and looking at him. It was Louie who had thrown the coconut. "I remember," said Baloo.

6. The shock of landing in the cold water and the sight of King Louie, had made Baloo remember the message. "I was supposed to tell Mowgli that you want him at your birthday party," said Baloo.

7. "I love birthday parties," smiled Mowgli. "Fancy you forgetting to tell me!" Baloo blushed. "It has ended happily," he said as King Louie led Mowgli and Baloo to the ruined temple, the home of King Louie. When they arrived they found the party in full swing. They joined in with the dancing immediately. "Many happy returns, Your Majesty!" everybody cheered. Then King Louie made an announcement. "Hidden around is some extra food in case you get hungry." *Can you find what has been hidden?*

Three bananas, three coconuts and a bunch of grapes.

SCAMP—THE HERO

1. It was a lovely sunny day. Lady and the Tramp took their puppy, Scamp, for a walk in the park. Suddenly, they heard a yelping and a squealing and a rush of running paws.

2. A group of dogs came racing by with a big, snarly dog chasing after them. "Growl! Yap! Yap!" barked the big dog. He was laughing and enjoying himself as he chased the others.

3. "Who is that nasty, rough dog?" asked Lady, who was always very gentle herself. "Oh, a new dog in the neighbour-hood," replied Tramp. He likes to throw his weight about."

4. While his mother and father strolled on, Scamp had a good think. "That new dog should not be allowed to bully the other dogs," he thought. "I'll show him."

5. "Come along, Scamp. Stop day-dreaming," Lady called as she and Tramp waited for their little pup. Scamp took no notice. He *was* a scamp!

6. The cheeky little pup ran up to the big bullying dog. "I think you should leave the other dogs alone," yapped Scamp. The big dog laughed.

7. "I don't care what you think!" sneered the big dog. "Go away, you shrimp!" Brave Scamp bared his teeth and snarled back: "I won't go away. I know what is right."

8. "It isn't right for you to bully the other dogs," growled Scamp. "You stop it and leave them alone or I will nip your ankles and I have sharp little teeth, I can tell you."

9. The big dog was so amazed that anyone had the courage to stand up to him, that he turned and slunk away. "Our Scamp is a hero," smiled the Tramp.

10. When they saw that the big dog had gone, the other dogs came crowding round Scamp. "Thank you. How did you get rid of him?" they asked. "I stood up to him like a real hero," boasted Scamp — and really he was right.

FRIAR TUCK'S

1. Long ago, when Robin Hood roamed in Sherwood Forest, he had a friend called Friar Tuck. Friar Tuck wore a long gown. It could be quite a nuisance, especially when it dragged in muddy puddles.

2. "Drat this long gown! It's quite useless!" grumbled Friar Tuck, brushing at the mud on his hem. Robin grinned.

3. A little later, Robin Hood and Little John, his big friend, had more to think about than Friar Tuck and his long gown. The Sheriff of Nottingham was on the prowl.

4. The Sheriff was collecting taxes from the poor villagers. Suddenly – WHAM! An arrow screeched over the Sheriff's head.

5. The Sheriff did not care for that sort of thing, not when the arrows were aimed at him, anyway. "Only Robin Hood would dare to shoot at me," he yelled. "After him, lads!" Off he ran.

LONG GOWN

6. The Sheriff was in such a rage that he ran off, leaving the box of taxes behind. That was a bad mistake. In a moment, Little John snatched up the box and ran away with it. He met Friar Tuck.

7. Now the Sheriff of Nottingham never forgot about money for long. He soon remembered the box of taxes and raced back for it. It was gone!

8. "Someone has taken the money and I want it back," screamed the Sheriff. "Which way! Which way did they go?" The answer was confusing.

9. The villagers were on Little John's side and they pointed in two directions. Even so, the Sheriff and his men caught up with Little John. He was chatting quietly.

10. "You dog! You stole my money!" yelled the Sheriff but Little John had no money and the Sheriff ran on.

11. The money had been hidden under Friar Tuck's gown. "Long gowns *are* useful," smiled the villagers, who now had their money back!

FUN-TIME *for everyone!*

If you shade in the dotted areas you will see Hiawatha and his buffalo chum.

Join the dots from No. 1 to No. 60 to see one of the funny folk from the film *Bedknobs and Broomsticks.* Could it be Oscar Ostrich?

The White Rabbit has lost his watch again! Help him to find it by leading him through the maze, without crossing a line.

Mickey's picnic

It was summertime. The weather was hot. Mickey Mouse decided to have a picnic.

He invited Minnie Mouse, his girl friend, and his two nephews, Morty and Ferdy.

Mickey made a big, pink-iced, cherry cake and he made a lot of small cakes, all with cherries on. He made two pies and a plate of sandwiches. He went out and bought four bottles of lemonade.

It was a very good picnic.

Minnie Mouse called round in the morning and looked at the food and *she* said that it was a very good picnic.

"Why don't we make the picnic perfect by telling everyone to behave properly?" said Minnie. "Those two nephews of yours have been getting out of hand lately, Mickey. I wish you would teach them some good manners so that when they are grown up, people will be pleased to invite them out. It is your duty."

"Very well," agreed Mickey, who always found it easier to agree with Minnie than to argue with her.

"Right," smiled Minnie. "I will be here for the picnic at four o'clock. No-one may start eating until we are all here, and sandwiches must be eaten before the cakes. That's the way my grandmother always told me things should be done."

"Very well," agreed Mickey.

Afternoon came. Mickey put out the picnic things. Then he sat in a chair to keep his eye on them. The warm weather made Mickey feel drowsy, and very soon he was asleep.

He did not hear his nephews arrive. He didn't see them sitting down to the picnic. He didn't hear them opening and drinking the lemonade. It was only when they argued about which cake to eat first that Mickey woke up.

"Stop eating the cakes before the sandwiches," he gasped. "Stop eating at all. Stop drinking."

The nephews stared at him. "What sort of picnic is this?" they asked.

"This is the sort of picnic where your Auntie Minnie will be *furious* with me if you start eating before she arrives," gasped Mickey.

They just managed to fetch some more lemonade and put the food straight before Minnie walked in.

PHEW! What a relief for Mickey and his nephews.

Alice and the Mad Hatter's Hat

1. A little girl named Alice, was having some very strange adventures in Wonderland. She went to have a cup of tea with the Mad Hatter, but his hat blew away.

2. "Help me catch the hat! Help me catch th hat!" shouted the March Hare. "Oh, ver well," said Alice.

3. "I suppose I must make myself agreeable if I wish to be invited to tea," thought Alice. She ran along at the side of the March Hare. The hat fell into the river.

4. SPLASH! Keeping all his clothes on, t March Hare dived into the river and pulled o the hat.

5. The Hatter left the river water in the hat. He put it on. Water splashed all over him. SWOOSH.

6. "Would you care to dance?" the Mad Hatter asked Alice. "No, thank you," she replied. "I would rather have some tea." "How selfish!" snapped the Hatter. "Your drinking tea will not make me dry. Dancing would have." They all sat down to tea.

7. "I am not selfish," said Alice, eating a cake. "You are foolish for putting on a hat without looking to see if it was full of water." "Do *you* always look in *your* hats to see if they are full of water?" chimed in the Hare. "Of course, I don't." Alice sighed.

****

Dot~to~dot fun with Mowgli

1. Mowgli was a human boy who was brought up in the jungle with the animals. Here he is with a big friend.

2. Join the dots from 1 to 25 and you will see who it is. Then you can find the three bananas hidden in the picture.

Cinderella tells a story about LAMBERT

1. This is a story about Lambert, the little lion who thought he was a lamb.

2. Lambert had been brought up by a mummy sheep and thought he was a lamb, but the other lambs could see he was not. "You have no white woolly coat," they said.

3. "Please let me play with you," begged Lambert. The lambs told him to count to one hundred while they went off to hide. Lambert smiled.

4. However, the lambs had no intention of playing Hide and Seek with Lambert. While *he* counted, *they* ran away up the mountain to play Follow My Leader.

5. The wild coyote in the mountain cave knew the lambs liked playing Follow My Leader. He dressed a baby coyote in a white woolly coat to look like a lamb.

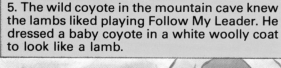

6. "Walk in front of those silly lambs and bleat 'BAAA-BAAA'" said the big coyote. "Then lead them back to our cave. Yum! Yum!"

8. Luckily, Lambert's searching took him up the mountain. He saw the lambs being led along by the coyote in disguise.

7. Meanwhile Lambert had finished counting to one hundred. He was disappointed not to find the lambs hiding nearby. He searched and searched.

9. Thinking that the coyote was a lamb, Lambert jumped on to it, shouting: *"Got you!"* He was amazed when the white woolly coat slipped off.

10. "We almost fell into a trap. Lambert, you saved us!" bleated the lambs, smiling at Lambert for once. Lambert put on the coyote's white woolly coat.

11. For all the rest of that day the lambs let Lambert play with them. He *was* happy!

BOILED STRING

1. Thousands of years ago, nearly all of Great Britain was covered by forest. The Ancient Britons lived in the forest and when they were hungry, they went out hunting for meat.

2. People ate a lot of meat in those days. It was before the potato had come from America. Three Ancient Britons called Mickey, Donald and Goofy went hunting. Goofy's arrow went astray.

3. The arrow hit Donald just where it made it uncomfortable for him to sit. Donald was furious. Fortunately, Mickey came along with a plump deer, which they roasted for their supper.

4. The lads were enjoying a fine supper of roast deer, bread, apples, honey and mead, when they heard the tramp of heavy boots. Mickey walked out and saw Roman soldiers.

5. Now all the Ancient Britons knew about Romans and how they liked to conquer, but this was the first time they had been seen in Britain. Mickey ran home.

"The Romans are coming. The Romans are [co]ming!" he cried. "Hide our food. Pretend we [ha]ve nothing to eat. Perhaps the Romans will go [an]d conquer someone else." Goofy and Donald [ru]shed to do as Mickey said.

7. Then Mickey had what seemed like a clever idea, but didn't turn out clever. "Let's get out those awful cheese straws Donald made and say they are string and that is all we have to eat," he said. So they did.

[When] the Romans burst into [th]e chums' little hut, Mickey [sa]id: "This is a terrible place, O, [Ro]man Lords. We only have [str]ing to eat. We are not worth [co]nquering. Please go away." [Th]e Roman commander, whose [na]me was General Spaghetti, [to]ok a forkful of the string and [at]e some. "I always like to try the [loc]al food," he smiled.

9. To Mickey's dismay, General Spaghetti thought that the 'string' was delicious. "I shall name this food after me," he smiled. "From now on it will be known as *spaghetti.*" He picked Mickey up and kissed him. "And you, you clever little Ancient Briton, must come back to Italy and make spaghetti for every-one in Rome." So Mickey and his friends had to go back to Rome, which they did not want to do. However, the trip through France was interesting and Rome *was beautiful,* so things could have been worse.

A train-ride for the Dalmatians

1. It's Cinderella again to tell you a story about the one hundred and one Dalmatians.

2. After all their adventures, the Dalmatians settled down happily to live with Roger and Anita, their human master and mistress. On television one afternoon, they watched a story about a train.

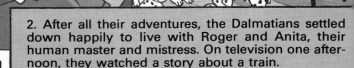

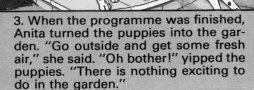

3. When the programme was finished, Anita turned the puppies into the garden. "Go outside and get some fresh air," she said. "Oh bother!" yipped the puppies. "There is nothing exciting to do in the garden."

4. Then one of the pups noticed a gap in the hedge between their garden and the garden next door. "Let's go exploring!" he yelped. He squirmed through the hole.

5. As it happened, a family with a little boy had recently moved to live next door. This little boy had left his toy train in the garden. The pups started to play with it.

6. The Dalmatians pretended they were having an adventure like the television story.

7. Then Roger saw them. "Stop that at once!" he shouted. "That is not your train." He went to speak to the people who lived next door.

8. "I am sorry my naughty puppies have meddled with the train," he said. Luckily, the little boy liked puppies and he was happy to play with them.

9. The little boy ran up and down the garden, giving the puppies rides in the train. They pretended they were driving through the Wild West with Indians chasing them.

10. What a happy afternoon everyone had! The puppies were pleased with their day.

Disneyland

Have fun trying to find out who can follow a clear path through the maze to the Disneyland Castle.

POOH THINKS THOUGHTS

One sunny morn Pooh Bear thought this:
"I feel like thinking thoughts today!"
So to his Thoughtful Spot he skipped
And on the ground, he there did lay.

Then Tigger came along and laughed:
"Stop thinking, Pooh! Do as I bid –
"For thinking thoughts is awfully dull –
"Let's go play games!" And so they did.

Bambi an

Bambi was a fawn and Thumper was a cheeky rabbit. They lived in the same part of the forest.

Thumper had a lot of friends and relations. He was always chatting to people and finding things out. He knew quite a lot more than Bambi.

One day, Thumper saw an old empty bird's nest lying on the ground. Nearby, were some white pebbles shaped like bird's eggs.

"I will play a joke on Bambi," smiled Thumper. "I can always do with a laugh." Thumper put the pebbles into the nest and called Bambi over to look at them. "This nestful of eggs must have fallen from the tree," said Thumper. "Don't you think you should tell Mrs. Bird. She may want to carry the nest back up into the tree and look after the little eggs."

"Oh, yes. Of course," agreed Bambi, who had a kind heart.

He stood under the branch on which Mrs. Bird was sitting. "Mrs. Bird," called Bambi. "Would you like to take care of this nestful of eggs?"

The bird flew down and looked at the pebbles in the old, worn-out nest. She knew at once that they were pebbles and not eggs, but she did not want to make Bambi look foolish because he was such a good-natured young deer. The bird glanced across at Thumper. She had seen what he had done.

"Thank you, Bambi. You are kind," smiled the bird. "I will take this nest of eggs up into the tree." Thumper was amazed when he saw Mrs. Bird pick up the nest in her beak and fly up into the tree.

"What a silly bird!" grumbled Thumper. "She was supposed to tell you that those were not eggs but pebbles, and I was gong to have a good laugh at you, Bambi. But Mrs. Bird really thought those pebbles were eggs. I don't know what has come over birds lately. They used to be

e bird's nest

...ver!''

...BONKETY-BONK! BONKETY-
...NK! BONK! BONK!

...Thumper had a surprise. Mrs. Bird
...vered high above his head and then
... go of the nest. The pebbles and the
...st broke into pieces and came
...mbling down on Thumper's head.

...''That will teach you to try to make a
...ol of little Bambi,'' squawked the
...d, as she flew away.

...''Gosh, Thumper! I hope you're not
...rt,'' gasped Bambi.

...''Oh, no. I'm not hurt,'' grumbled
...umper, ''but I think it's a shame that
...-one in the forest wants to enjoy a
...gh any more.''

...Mrs. Bird flew back and landed by
...mbi. ''Come with me and I will
...ch you how to tell real eggs from
...bbles and lots of other useful
...ngs,'' she chirped. ''The forest can
... dangerous for little chaps who
...n't know very much.''

...Bambi went with Mrs. Bird for that
...y. However, the next day, Bambi
...d Thumper were friends again.
...ey stayed friends until they were
...th grown up. Bambi became a
...and stag with huge antlers and was
...e king of the forest.

...Thumper became nothing more
...portant than a jolly bunny rabbit,
...t he was always dashing here and
...ere and chatting to all his friends
...d relations. He learned a lot about
...ho came into the forest and who
...ent out of the forest. He always
...ew when trees were to be felled or
...here the humans liked to eat their
...cnics.

...He knew where the greenest grass
...ew and where the ripe forest fruit
...as to be found.

...He was a very useful little friend to
...ng Bambi.

...However, Thumper still likes to
...ugh and play tricks so Bambi was
...ways careful to see that Thumper
...d not trick him.